THE COMPLETE POETIC OF PHO

I'm Phoebe Flood and th[ese are my] works up to now. But by the time you read this they won't be, because I will have written some more poems. Frankly, I don't see how you can ever catch up. I am at present at work on a novel. Actually, I'm not, but poets always say that because they don't think that writing poems all day is a real job. I know a few poets. Well, one really, and that's what he says. I'm not going to tell you much more about myself because there's quite a lot of that in the poems. And in the other bits I put in.

Some people are dweeby
With brains at a low ebb.
They don't think it's PHOEBE,
They think that it's FO-EBB.

Likewise I'm not rude
Or stick-in-the-mud
But it just isn't FLEWD,
It is FLOOD -

PHOEBE FLOOD (dweeby crud)

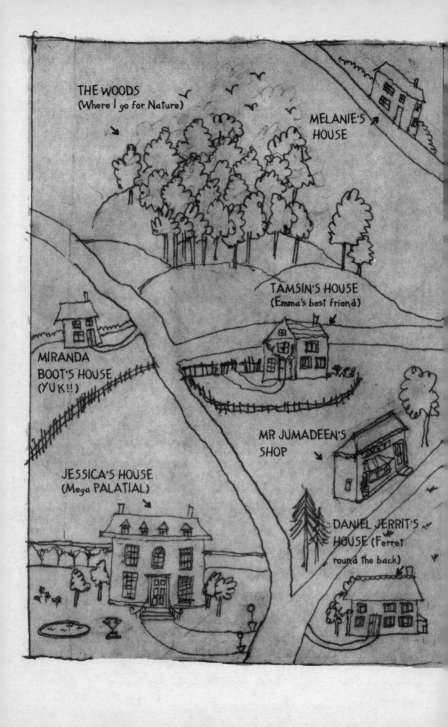

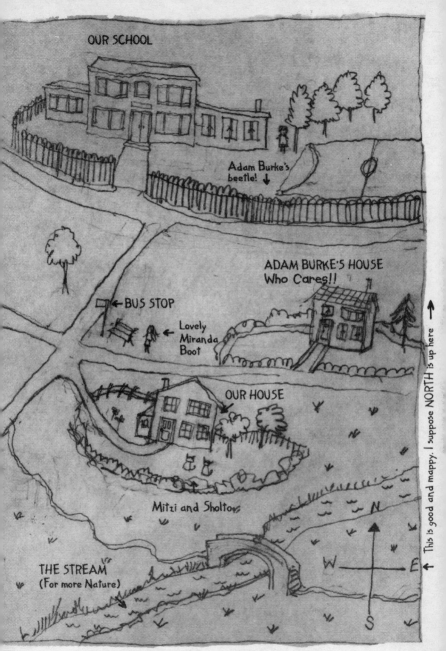

OUR SCHOOL

Adam Burke's beetle! ↓

ADAM BURKE'S HOUSE
Who Cares!!

← BUS STOP

Lovely Miranda Boot ←

OUR HOUSE

Mitzi and Sholto

THE STREAM
(For more Nature)

This is good and mappy. I suppose NORTH is up here →

N
W — E ←
S

P.S. There are other houses but these are the IMPORTANT ones!

For Ellie and Katie

Text copyright © 1997 John Whitworth
Illustrations copyright © 1997 Lauren Child

Designed by Dave Crook

Published by Hodder Children's Books 1997

ISBN 0340 68134 9

Hodder Children's Books
A division of Hodder Headline plc
338 Euston Road
London NW1 3BH

Printed and bound in Great Britain by
Cox & Wyman Ltd, Reading, Berkshire

THE COMPLETE POETICAL WORKS OF PHOEBE FLOOD

introduced by John Whitworth
illustrations by Lauren Child

Hodder
Children's
Books

a division of Hodder Headline plc

CONTENTS

IMPRESSIVE, HUH!!

 PROFILE

NAME: Phoebe Fern Fitzbronte-Shakespeare Flood

FAMOUS FOR: Poetry. Or I soon will be.

BORN: I wasn't produced by binary fission, you know. My Mum and Dad are quite ordinary. They go on about bills and how good The Beatles were but in other ways are OK.

LIVES: There's a map at the front of the book. A bit Winnie-The-Pooh if you ask me, but my nice publisher insisted.

BROTHERS AND SISTERS: Afraid so. Did you know that if you're an only child, you're statistically more likely to be rich and famous. So I'm succeeding against the odds.

My brother Justin is interested in football and girls and skin cleansing. MEGA BORING, say me and my sister. He says we're sad. He hasn't got a very big vocabulary but he's OK and anyhow he's IN LOVE so you can't blame him.

My sister Emma is very brilliant though also very young. I don't actually mind because I am an Artist and don't have to be clever, only Artistic. She wants to be an Astronaut, not a very right-on thing. As I said, she's very young.

PETS: Cats called Sholto and Mitzi. I share a hamster. I once had a snail called Hamlet. She was released into the wild.

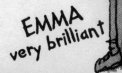
EMMA
very brilliant

HOBBIES: Improving my mind.

FAVE MUSIC: Mozart's Sonata in B Flat Major, K. 333, played by Charles Rosen on the Siena Pianoforte, since you ask.

FAVE FOOD: I don't spend my life thinking about food like some people, but I wouldn't say no to a Neapolitan Sundae With Hot Fudge Sauce if you're buying.

STAR SIGN: Libra with Scorpio rising. Sun in Leo. Moon in Cancer. I just copied that off an old magazine. I wonder what it means.

DESCRIBE YOUR LOOK: You have to be joking.

WHO DO YOU FANCY? Seamus Heaney has very nice eyebrows. There is a boy called Adam Burke who expects to be here but he isn't, so ha-ha.

WHOSE POSTER DO YOU HAVE ON YOUR WALL? William Shakespeare. He has nice eyebrows too. I also have one of an orca jumping and a short-eared owl but they don't count.

MESSAGE TO THE WORLD: Poetry will save the planet.

MY ROOM

MESSAGE TO WHOM
IT MAY CONCERN
THAT'S YOU, YOU MEGACRUD

THIS IS THE ROOM
OF PHOEBE FERN
FITZBRONTE-SHAKESPEARE FLOOD

SO HEAR THE WORD
MY DOOR IS TOUGH
AND LOCKED WITH IRON BOLTS

AND ANY NERD
THAT TOUCHES STUFF
GETS 20,000 VOLTS

TRESPASSERS NOT
IMPALED, ENTOMBED
OR STUNG TO DEATH BY BEES

ARE DROWNED IN SNOT
AND THEN CONSUMED
BY MARTIAN WORM DISEASE

SO KEEP IN MIND
THAT THE ABOVE
IS WRITTEN OUT IN BLOOD

AND SEALED AND SIGNED
BY ORDER OF

PHOEBE - THE POET - FLOOD

This is particularly for brothers who don't
know the meaning of PRIVATE.

WHEN I AM FAMOUS

I don't actually know anyone famous though Eric Gossage was once on one of those TV shows where you leap into deep pools of gunge and everybody cheers. He got a Mr Blobby T-shirt for it.

When I am famous on TV
Presenter of THE POETS' SHOW
Everyone will be nice to me.

I'll get invited out to tea
And sometimes I'll agree to go
When I am famous on TV.

Though green with envy secretly
The dweebs and dorks I used to know
Will be especially nice to me.

'It was a privilege to be
Her friend. We always said she'd grow
Up mega-famous on TV–

Such charm, such grace, such modesty!
Her whole complexion seems to glow!'
(They go on being nice to me.)

'Cute looks! Great personality!
A genius from top to toe!'
When I am famous on TV
Everyone will be nice to me.

THE QUEEN AND HER SERVANTS

This is a problem that has often worried me.

When the Queen gets up each morning
Do the servants make her bed?
Do the servants dunk her teabag?
Do the servants toast her bread?

When the Queen is in the shower
Do the servants hold the soap?
And when she sends a letter
Do they lick the envelope?

When she's hoovering the Palace
Do the servants really hoover?
And let her hold the sucky end
While they sort of manoeuvre?

Do they walk the royal corgis?
Do they feed the royal cats?
Do they shine the royal handbags?
Do they brush the royal hats?

Do they hold the Queen's umbrella
When she's stood out in the rain?
And when she's finished in the loo
Do the servants pull the chain?

My life's not at all like that.

OH WHAT A BEAUTIFUL

From Monday to Friday
You get yourself tidy
At 7 o'clock in the morning.
Your dad's in pyjamas
And going bananas
Because he can't stop himself yawning.

You're late for the bus and
You're all of a fuss and
The cats are creating a racket.
The milk's gone all whiffy,
The bread's pretty iffy,
The cereal's dead in the packet.

Your mum and your brother
Are cross with each other
They're banging around in the kitchen.
It's something to do
With a shirt that went blue
In the wash and a cuff that needs stitching.

Your sweet little sister's
A wart and a blister
Who's dropped buttered toast on your jotter.
'Can I take the day off, Mum?
I'm starting a cough. Mum,
I don't want to go!' But you've gotta.

There's a mouse in the toilet.
The kettle won't boil – it
Makes tea that's decidedly cool.
You could burst into tears and
This goes on for years and
It's called

GETTING READY FOR SCHOOL.

Actually I'm fine in the mornings. It's just the
rest of the family that's awful.

THE ORANGE POEM

My teacher Miss Hornbeam says there aren't
any rhymes for orange. She says there aren't
any rhymes for silver either, but I haven't done
a silver poem yet.

Though you couldn't have an orange
In the prehistoric forenge

(because there were only ferns and things)

And the rabbits in their warrenges
Like lettuce more than oranges

(who wants to be a rabbit anyway?)

Breakfast porrenge is quite horrenge-juice
You'd better have an orange-juice

(they eat it in Scotland standing up for some reason)

Children wouldn't ever quarrenge
If they'd only eat an orange

(it's the vitamin C my friend says)

There's a girl called Florenge Morrenge
And she always shares her orange

(and her vanilla yoghurt too which I really like)

THE POETS' PARTY

These are all the names of real poets in case you thought I made some of them up for the rhymes. I could have put in 'Phoebe Flood likes a baked spud', but that would be boasting which I never do. Putting myself in with Shakespeare is what would be boasting, not liking baked spuds.

Percy Bysshe Shelley
likes strawberry jelly,
taking turns
With Rabbie Burns,
             but
John Keats
sucks sweets
and Roger McGough, he
sucks toffee.

Michael Rosen
has chosen
to eat venison
with Lord Tennyson,
             but
Wendy Cope
Wants grilled antelope,
though Ted Hughes
prefers stews.

Christina Rossetti
cries, 'Give me spaghetti!'
as John Milton
bellows, 'More Stilton!'
                    but
Philip Larkin
nibbles parkin
and William Butler Yeats
pigs it on nuts and dates.

Geoffrey Chaucer
slurps tea from a saucer
as Seamus Heaney
sips Dry Martini,
                    but
William Shakespeare
takes beer –
tippling
with Rudyard Kipling.

17

I am a little on the plump side, so I know what it's like. Ben Jonson, a great poet and a friend of Shakespeare, had a mountain of a belly, which must be VERY FAT. So has the Buddha, one of the greatest people who has ever lived, and Saint Thomas Aquinas, who was a Saint, which must count for something.

People say
YOU'RE FAT

I don't worry about that
I say
But I do
Mirrors say
YOU'RE FAT

I don't worry about that
I say

It's not true

Adam Burke he
Eats and eats
Ice-cream
Chocolate
Pickled Onion Monster Munch
Sherbert sweets
Also his lunch

Stuffing stuff in like a hamster
Like a VULTURE if it comes to

That
But he's
NOT FAT

It isn't fair and I don't care
I say

But I do

SECOND POEM ABOUT FATNESS

Ivan the Terrible, who killed lots of people, and
George Joseph Smith, who killed three wives in
the bath (one after the other not all at once),
and Sherlock Holmes who I never liked, and
Dracula, were all THIN people.

Jason is a bully
the toughest in the class
he drags you by the pully
and throws you on the grass

Jason is a rat
Jason says YOU'RE HORRIBLY HORRIBLY
HORRIBLY FAT
Jason is a pig
I say ACTUALLY I'M **BIG**

I get him down and I sit on his face and then
He gets so scared he sicks up in the basin and
Everyone cheers at the taming of Jason and

I wasn't fat I was strong
I knew I was all along

Jason's my friend now actually

SOMETIMES

When I did ballet Mum used to call me
Tumbleova which has probably got something to
do with it. Tumbleova is a kind of a joke, though
not very hilarious.

Sometimes when my mum
thinks she is quite alone
she dances
        oh just a few steps

she's pegging out washing
or cooking stuff or just

I don't know
staring out of the
window halfway upstairs

and she dances
        just a few steps

I think I'm a Pavlova
she said once smiling

but I really think
even at your age Mum
You're more than a pudding really

PIANO PLAYING

The problem with my dad and the piano is he gets really cross when it doesn't do what he wants and he swears and bangs the keys which isn't at all good for them. Then Mum says, 'Language, dear!' and things get stressed. But he does try, which is very good for someone his age. He can play 'She'll be Coming Round the Mountain' quite well if he gets the first bit right.

When I started piano
My dad started too.
He said it was something
He'd wanted to do.

He couldn't afford
To take lessons like I did
But worked on the pieces
My teacher provided.

He found it quite hard
For his hands were too fat
And his brain was too old
And excuses like that.

22

I said to him, 'Dad
You must work every day
And little by little
I'll show you the way.'

'You must practise and practise
And never forget.
Will you do it?' I said
And my dad said, 'You bet!'

And he did. So today
We can play...

  a DUET.

    (well nearly)

I've always been embarrassed to say this so I hope someone will get the message though I have to say he's not exactly subtle so he might not. In which case I shall quietly go bananas.

Dad – when you
pick me up from school
I like it
except for
one teensy-weensy
little thing
which I don't
want to mention in
case it hurts
your feelings
(Dad I know you do
have feelings
though being
a man you pretend
to be tough
and bluff and
rough and stuff like that)
well you see
what it is
that teensy-weensy
little thing
it's well it's
that scrumpy sort of
hat you wear
to hide the
bald bit - Dad I wish
you wouldn't.

Emma's favourite book is 'Matilda' by Roald Dahl. It's her favourite book because it's about a very clever little girl who is misunderstood by her family. I have to say it's very good.

Justin being eldest
Gets everything first
Naturally...

Do I care?
Yes a lot.

Emma being youngest
Is sweetest as neat as
Can be...

Is it fair?
No it's not.

But look down the kid list
And guess who's the middlest?

ME!

(I could swear
You forgot)

Emma   Phoebe   Justin   Mum   Dad

FRIENDS

Me and my friend Melanie
    stick like glue
We're together in
    all we do
Making up the
    gang of two

Best friends always
    like to share.
I've got her Bugs Bunny
    socks to wear
She's got my dinosaur
    knickers – so there!

We share a hamster and
    he comes in
Morning assembly in a
    cocoa tin
He runs up Jessica's
    bare skin

Jessie yells her head off
    (she should boil it)
Just a teeny hamster and
    she has to spoil it
Shove her stupid head down
    the junior toilet

Jessie's best friend pulls

Melanie's hair
Jessie breaks my glasses it's
    not fair
We get told off
    don't care

Yack-Yack-Yackety
    drop dead
Jessie gets the giggles and
    teacher gets red
ALL OF YOU GIRLS GO
 SEE THE HEAD

Megamonster SHOUT from
    orang-utang
Now there's four in
    our gang –
Duffing up of teachers
    CRASH!
        ERK!
            BANG!

Orang-utang is a bit rude for a Head, but he does have extremely long arms and hair on his back which you can see when he's changing for refereeing. He's far too old to play football.

27

Ursula Veitch never talks to anyone except her friend Sharon Teakle and her iguana. But she writes poetry in maths lessons. This is a triolet but if you're not a poet you don't have to know that. Triolets are good to write because you get eight lines for the price of five, if you see what I mean.

My Unicorn
How Beautiful
In Dew of Dawn
My Unicorn
Washes his Horn
In the Forest Pool
My Unicorn
How Beautiful

$4 \times 4 \times 4 \times 4$

These are squarish poems with everything in fours – syllables, lines, verses, poems. They're suitable for Justin, my brother, because he is an angular sort of person and has some very sharp edges – particularly when I'm around.

I ALWAYS know
when my brother
really fancies
anybody

savage zits in
close formation
battle pattern
concentrate their

operations
on the very
tip of his nose
so I measure

(it's pathetic)
Justin's sex-life
by the profile
of his nose-zits

so our Justin's
in Love again
it's official
(it's pathetic)

honestly he
goes bright red when
he sees her at
the bus stop and

kicks bits out of
the wall (vandal)
and all the time
she chews her split

ends giggling (quelle
prat) and her name
is (wait for it)
Miranda Boot

Miranda Boot
(Justin's latest)
has long blonde hair
(to tell the truth

they've all got long
blonde hair) but she's
got a brace she
sort of clicks as

well and Emma
knows her kid sis-
ter Karly and
what she says is

Miranda's a
cow with a ter-
rible temper
ah love is blind

brrr-brrr brrr-brrr
could I speak to
Miranda please?
    this is the pub-

    lic library
    we are closed at
    present... (sugar)
    six nine two four

    three brrr-brrr brrr-
    hallo hallo
    could I speak to
Miranda please?

oh (suck finger)
well when will she
oh (scratch ear) no
there's no message

THE BRONTOSAURUS

You can't have a poetry book without dinosaur poems. The brontosaurus isn't the biggest dinosaur, (which is the seismosaurus) but I thought it was when I wrote this. I put '&' instead of 'and' because I love the poetry of Roger McGough.

NOTE: The seismosaurus lived in Albuquerque, USA, before there was an Albuquerque, of course. I got this from another good poet called Jack Prelutsky. So who says poets don't know stuff?

the brontosaurus lived when the earth was green
green leaves and creepers were what was to be seen
& greenly in his great body lives the brontosaurus

his eyes are watery & small between ferns & fronds
& flowerfood so roundabout deep quiet ponds
he takes his time having a great deal of time

his brain is in his nerve ends he thinks along his skin
his lungs consider breathing & all his huge within
considers digestion burping burping burping

rain falls on the brontosaurus now & it is good the
darkness slides up to him & it is as it should be
the brontosaurus stands where he stood
sleeps in the shadow of the wood

sleeps in the shadow
sleeps

PLAYING AT HOME

This is another one for Justin. His idea of Heaven, without Miranda Boot anyway, is spending every day sweaty and in shorts. Some of us grow out of that sort of thing. We are called girls. Others never do. They are called boys.

When the catch went down and the batsman grinned – oh
Who was the one that dropped it?
When the Junior Cup went out of the window
Who was the one that copped it?
Why is it always ME that muffs it?
Couldn't it sometimes be
Somebody else round the place that stuffs it?
Why is it always me?

The keeper flat with an open goal and
Over the bar I kick it.
Book me a train to the mines of Poland.
Book me a one-way ticket.
Why is it always me that's the failure,
Twit to the nth degree,
Someone that looks like a toad only scalier?
Why is it always me?

Back with the family playing Monopoly,
Who is it lands on Mayfair?
Someone up there isn't treating me properly.

Someone up there doesn't play fair.
Call me a wimp, a dweeb, an oaf, a
Rabbit, a chimpanzee.
Call me. I'm hiding behind the sofa.

WHY IS IT ALWAYS ME!

PLAY THE GAME

Our school never wins at games. It used to drive
Justin mad. And now he's at the big school and
he can't get into the football team because
they're all built like furniture vans and shave
three times a day. The boys I mean. I think I just
mean the boys. And as I've already told you, I
don't care about games. Life's too short to spend
it throwing a ball about.

By the way, why is it that if a girl's boyish
then it's all right, or even good, but if a boy's
girlish then it isn't at all?

At netball we lost twenty-nil
And my friend Jessie felt quite ill
You do when you lose twenty-nil.

King's Junior were MUCH TOO TALL
They cheated too. They pinched the ball.
It wasn't very fair at all.

Their cheaty ref's the one I blame
But my dad says it's just a game
And I suppose so. All the same

When Jessie told their ref to stick it
My dad says that just wasn't cricket.
Remember, Dad, what isn't cricket

The next time England lose a wicket.

NOAH'S DINOSAURS

Noah was sailing his ark with Mrs Noah.

The **horses** were horsing about.
The **goats** were playing the goat.
The **sheep** were looking sheepish.
The **pigs** were pigging out.
The **bulls** were bullish (but the cows were rather cowed).
The **dogs** kept dogging his footsteps.
The **cats** kept catting up their food.
The **flies** were flying.
The **slugs** were sluggish.
The **snails** went at a snail's pace and
The **budgies** wouldn't budge at all.
The **rain** was raining rainily.

The **doves** were lovey-dovey.
The **rats** were ratty.
The **bats** were batty.
The **lice** were lousy.
The **mice** were mousey.
The **elephants** were elephantine.
The **crocodiles** shed crocodile tears.
The **fish** round the ark all drank like fish.
The **flounders** were floundering and
The **tiddlers** were all tiddly.
The **whales** of course were having a whale of a time.

But the **dinosaurs** just sat there so glumly and gloomily
Playing cards in the corner so dumbly and doomily.
What was on the cards was extinction.

Noah said to Mrs Noah, 'You know,
I worry about the dinosaurs.'

LAST WORDS ON DINOSAURS

You know what a field of cows is like. I mean how
you've got to watch where you put your feet.
Imagine a field full of Brontosauruses. You could
suffocate if you weren't careful.

> In the time of the triceratops
> There weren't any shops.
>
> No Sainsburys or Marks
> Just Jurassic Parks.
>
> It wasn't a nice age
> Before the Ice Age.

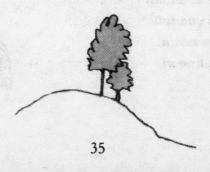

A NOISY NOISE ANNOYS

Perhaps this doesn't bother older people so much.
At the school disco mums and dads jig about like
crazy while we're outside away from the racket.
Of course, wrinklies could all be going deaf.

Lotta gotta
ghetto blaster,
gotta lotta
music HOT!

Hear the beat a-
long the street, a
treat for some, for
others not.

(Hey little lady-o,
can you can your radio?

Shan't! Shan't! Shan't!)

Wotta scandal!
Wotta vandal!
Lotta's not a
cat to know!

Wotta brat, an
utter rotter,
nutter with a
rad-i-o!

(The hills are alive
with the sound of mu-zak...

I can't stand it,
I can't stand it,

Lotta the decibel bandit)

So I gotta
black biretta
(not a hat – a
little gun)

and I shot her
nasty ghetto
blaster... wotta
lotta fun!

TEN QUIZ QUESTIONS

I think all poetry books should have a quiz. I
suppose the answers ought to be at the back of
the book. All right then, turn to the back of the
book (well, further on - page 106 for the answers.)

1. Why is Mickey Mouse black and white when
    nobody's ever seen a black and white mouse?

2. When you lose a glove and your mum buys you
    another pair and then you lose a glove again, why
    are the two gloves that you've got now both for the
    same hand?

3. Why does a computer keyboard say QWERTYUIOP
    and not ABCDEFGHIJ?

4. Why is wool itchy on you but not on sheep?

5. Why is it called a toothbrush when you've got more
    than one tooth?

6. What age will you be in Heaven?

7. Why does your hair grow but not your eyelashes?

8. Can people actually see those halo things saints
    have?

9. Why does the sun look bigger when it's setting.
    I mean it can't actually be bigger can it?

10. Why do people say my freckles are sweet when
    I hate them?

TIDY YOUR ROOM

Parents have got a sort of obsession, haven't they? I mean, you know perfectly well where everything is, but that isn't good enough. Do you think they're showing off to other parents, like you were a pet or something?

Tidying rooms is dumb,
Tidying rooms is sad,
But, till your brain is numb,

TIDY YOUR ROOM, says Mum,
TIDY YOUR ROOM, says Dad.

TIDY YOUR ROOM.

Funny what makes them glad –
Hoovering every crumb.
Tidying's just a fad,

TIDY YOUR ROOM, says Dad.

Sometimes it makes them glum,
Sometimes it makes them mad,
Volume at maximum,

TIDY YOUR ROOM, says Mum.

One thing I'd like to add
(OK – that's bubblegum)
This is my PRIVATE pad.

TIDY YOUR ROOM, says Dad,
TIDY YOUR ROOM, says Mum.

TIDY YOUR ROOM!

That last one was nearly a rondeau. Not many people can do them. Not even nearly.

JURASSIC FOREST

This is a sound poem and has to be PERFORMED. I perform it brilliantly but I'm not there so you will have to try it yourself as best you can. The oy oy oy is the cry of a small animal that hangs from the Jurassic trees, a sort of reptile monkey. People have asked me about that.

berzwiggle
                                                    oy
TUMFF   oy
PUMFF   oy
TUMFF
  oy   PUMFF

schrook schrook schrook   oy
berzwiggle   (oy)   oy
  oy   berzwiggle   (oy)   oy
berzwiggle

TUMFF   oy
  oy   PUMFF   oy
TUMFF   oy

oy
BOYYYYYLOKKKKK criddlecriddlecriddle
BEEEEEJYOM criddlecriddlecriddle (oy)

TUMFF PUMFF (oy) TUMFF criddlecriddle
PUMFF cri..... A
  oy   A
                    I   oy
                    I   oy
  oy   E   oy
                    E..... **SPLOTTTTT**GER_{GGG}G_{HOL} oy
oy oy oy

                                        oy
                          oy

                    oy

41

SONG OF THE GREAT AUK

The Great Auk was called the Northern Penguin and lived on uninhabited islands in the North Atlantic. Sailors caught them easily because they couldn't fly and didn't know about people. They killed the last one in 1844.

On the rocky
Barren islands
Diving, dipping
Through the water...

On the islands
Where we nested
Many thousands
Hundred thousands
In the breaking
North Atlantic
Turning, dipping
Through the water

We're stupid birds
We can't fly
We must die

Great Auks!
Great gawks!

Blackened firepits
Spitting cauldrons
See the sailors
See the killers
Rake the feathers
From the cauldrons
Hook the bodies
From the firepits

We're stupid birds
Run away
Hide away

Stand still!
Kill! Kill!

See the naked
Rotting bodies
On the barren
Stinking island
Hundred thousands
Hundred thousands
Bobbing, bobbing
In the water

We're stupid birds
Senseless things
Defenceless things

Wordless...
Bird Less...

43

IN DREAMS I AM A CROCODILE

Last Thursday, Miss Hornbeam said we should imagine we were our favourite animals. Adam Burke was pulling my jersey and I knew straight-away what I wanted to be.

In dreams I am a crocodile
Beside the waters of the Nile,
And all the while I smile and smile

Beside that dark Nilean flood,
Thudding my tail into the mud
As sunlight permeates my blood.

The pyramids are old, but I'm
Much older, twice as old as time.
I come from the primeval slime,

I am the god of goop and goo,
Of all that fashions you and you,
And everything I say is true.

My sun shines down without a pause.
My fish swim in and out my jaws
For I'm the one that makes the laws.

My whispering papyrus grass,
My tinkling bells as camels pass,
My wide white heaven still as glass,

My date palms and my camel trains,
My months of warm unending rains,
My smells like thirty thousand drains,

My moony hippopotami,
Their tuneful, croonful lullaby!
Ah, who could be content as I?

PEN FRIENDS

I don't know why teachers have this thing about
pen friends and writing letters as if the phone
had never been invented. I can't remember any
pen friend who's ever said anything at all
interesting. Emma says HER penfriend has a
South American python and a big sister who's on
Grange Hill but I bet she's making it up.

cutie pie bunny

Rosebud Cottage
Honeysuckle Lane
Little Twittering
Summersweetshire

Dear Phoebe

I am thrilled that we are going to be pen friends.
I am sure that we will like each other.

I live in a nice house with a nice garden.

I have a brother.
He is nice.

We have a pet rabbit.
We call him Bunny
He is very nice indeed.

We used to have a nice budgerigar.
He was called Budgie but he died.

The cat next door ate him.
The cat next door is not nice.
The cat next door is called Fleur Fairweather de Courcy.
I do not like the name much.

My hobby is collecting bottle tops.
I have 143 all different.

I don't know what I want to be when I grow up.
But I want things to be nice.

Your pen friend,

Cindy Sweet
P.S. Some people say I am pretty.

The Vaults
Castle Close

Skull Duggery
Transylvania

Dear Cindy

I am also thrilled that we are going to be pen friends.
How nice your domestic arrangements sound!

I am afraid I do not live in a nice house like you.
I live in a castle with slimy dungeons.
It also has a torture chamber.
Still it is home and I love it dearly.
So do all the other vampires.
Please come and visit us as soon as possible.
I will show you what my hobby is when you come.
Please bring your brother and your rabbit.
You will all be welcome.

My favourite book character is Peter Pan.
He never grew up.
Neither will you.

Your pen friend

Phoebe
Barebones Fern Fitzbronte-Shakespeare Flood
P.S. I am glad you are pretty.
P.P.S. When you come, please bring your Blood Donor card.

LETTER TO SEAMUS HEANEY

While we're on the subject of letters, poets are always sending letters to other poets. I chose Seamus Heaney because he is the most famous poet in the world besides being good. I mean he's not as famous as Shakespeare but Shakespeare's dead so I can hardly send him a letter, can I, dumbo? Seamus Heaney won The Nobel Prize for Literature, which is ever so much money, so you see poetry can be a worthwhile career just like chartered accounting.

I thought that I would write to you
Because I am a poet too.
I write a lot of poetry.
Some of it rhymes, as you can see.
Poems don't have to rhyme today.
I mean, yours don't and that's OK.

A poem that you wrote got read
In our Assembly by the Head,
All about Ireland, grass and rain.
I hope he reads it out again
When Jessica (she's my best mate)
Shuts up and I can concentrate.

My uncle keeps a pub in Sligo
I hope the weather's fine when I go.
Next holidays is when I do
I'd really like to call on you.
I know you're busy. Would there be time
For me to come at Sunday teatime?

I'll bring some poems round, and we
Can read stuff out alternately.
Then you can tell me (if you would)
Which ones of mine you think are good.
You are quite old and VERY wise.
Congratulations on your Prize.

P.S.
I like crumpets by the way.
I hope it isn't rude to say.

P.P.S.
And of course I know to call you Shaymus

49

My friend Jessica says my book should have a soap. She likes them.

THE BLOAT FILES

Chapter One

Horace Bloat was the richest person in England. Not counting the Queen of course. He woke up one morning and felt bad. He called for his guitar and began to sing.

> Well I woke up this morning
> And I didn't feel good.
> Yes I woke up this morning,
> Didn't feel like I should.
> My body was kinda lumpy
> And my head was made of wood.

He still felt bad. He thought he would count his money to cheer himself up. He called for his CD-ROM.

The figures clicked up. £4,722,211,948.25p. They went on clicking. The interest on his money was a hundred pounds a second.

He paid himself a round figure bonus. £100,000.00p was very round indeed. £4,722,311,948.25p! That was about the size of it now. He liked the size of it.

But he still felt bad. He took up his guitar again.

Well I woke up this morning
And I felt real mean.
Yes I woke up this morning
Like a mean machine.
Man I mean I was the meanest
Mean machine there's ever been.

Outside was The Horace Bloat Fish Glue Factory plc
where ten thousand peasants scuttled to and fro.

'Grovel!' Horace cried from the window.

Ten thousand peasants bowed and scraped.

'Enough! Get your fishy fingers out!'

'Three bags full, Boss!' They scuttled even faster.

Horace felt better. 'Bloat,' he said to himself, 'a change
is as good as a rest and it's a change you need. I
wish...'

POP! There at the door was a sweet, white-haired old
lady wearing a SAVE THE WHALES badge.

'Fairy-godmother!' cried Horace. 'At last!'

Continued on page 80

51

BURYING THE BIRD

This was me and Jessica. It was Sholto that pulled the poor thing through the cat door. But he's not to blame because that's the way cats are. It was buried under the rhubarb because that wouldn't get dug up. Rhubarb's another of those words that doesn't have a rhyme. I suppose rhubarby would rhyme with 'Oooo Barbie!' but that isn't very suitable.

We buried the bird today.

We brought it out on a tray,
Its look was stiff and its feel was chill,
And its eyes were shut and its heart was still.

We buried the bird today.

It was a baby jay,
Its beak was black and its wing was blue,
It was dead as the meat on a barbecue.

We buried the bird today.

Flat on its back it lay,
And both of our cats came sniffing round,
As we found our spot and we dug the ground.

We buried the bird today.

Last night it was quite OK,
And we fed it a worm and we fed it a fly,
And we thought last night that it wouldn't die.

We buried the bird today.

There wasn't a lot to say,
What was warm flesh and blood is just cold skin and
  bone,
So we scratched its name on a piece of stone.

We buried the bird today.

The sky was all scribbly grey,
Grey as the stone of a pyramid,
And it sat on the world like a dustbin lid.

We buried the bird today.

The shoebox was lined with hay
And flowers and leaves and a pigeon feather,
And we laid the bird in the earth together,

For ever.

The way cats are!

BREAKING UP

It was all just a silly misunderstanding. She thought I said something to Melanie that I never did and so she said... but I'm not one to bear a grudge. As for the 'Just Seventeen's' that's not true and anyway she doesn't keep them there now. Also, considering the newspaper her dad reads, he's got a bit of a cheek quite frankly.

We're finished as best friends. This time it's for good.
Jess and me is all over. No way can we make up.
What d'you say? No, it's none of it my fault — she could
Take it back, what she said, but she won't. It's the
      break-up.

I walked home from school on my own. She was talking
To Emily Hogg at the gate. She pretended
She just didn't see me. I kept right on walking
Alone. By myself. So our friendship has ended.

It's better like this. All my homework's been done now.
I won't have to copy off Melanie under
The desk like I used to. And *Neighbours* is fun now.
I never could follow the story. No wonder

With Jessica gossipping yackety-yack.
She's so shallow. Her stuff about boys is so sad.
All those *Just Seventeens* that she keeps at the back
Of the box in her garage because of her dad.

Don't care if we don't read the letters together.
Don't care if she doesn't ring up for a chat.
Don't care AT ALL about Jessica, whether
She lives or she dies makes no difference. What's that?

Well, if it's the phone I'm not answering ever.
Oh all right then... Who's that?... Oh it's you... See
        here Jess...
If you think I... What?... You're not serious?... She
        never!...
Bring your bike round and tell me... In half an hour?

        YES!

DRAGONS

You can write this type of poem on a computer
when other people are doing technology with
cereal packets. If they say how will you get on in
the real world not knowing technology you can
tell them there are jobs as poets but none
making things out of cereal packets.

```
                    s                           s
                   nsd                         nsd
                  onsdr                       onsdr
                 gonsdra                     gonsdra
                 agonsdrag                   agonsdrag
                 ragonsdrago                 ragonsdrago
                 dragonsdragon               dragonsdragon
                 sdragonsdragons             sdragonsdragons
               nsdragon dragonsdragonsdragon dragonsd
            onsdrago     ragonsdragonsdrago     ragonsdr
            gonsdrag      agonsdragonsdrag       agonsdra
            agonsdra       gonsdragonsdra         gonsdrag
            ragonsdr        onsdragonsdr           onsdrago
            dragonsd         nsdragonsd             nsdragons
            dragonsdr        onsdragonsdr          onsdragons
            ragonsdra       gonsdragonsdra        gonsdragon
            agonsdrag      ragonsdragonsdrag      agonsdrago
            gonsdrago   dragonsdragonsdrago    dragonsdrag
              onsdragonsdragonsdragonsdragonsdragonsdra
              nsdragonsdragonsdragonsdragonsdragonsdr
               sdragonsdragonsdragonsdragonsdragonsd
                gonsdragonsdragonsdragonsdrag
                 onsdragonsdragonsdragonsdra
                  nsdragonsdragonsdragonsdr
                   sdragonsdragonsdragonsd
                   dragonsdragonsdragons
                   dragonsdragonsdragons
                   dragonsdragonsdragons
                    gons   go   rag
                    onsd   go   dra
                    nsdr   go   sdr
                     sdragonsd
                      dragons
                       ragon
                        ago
```

Justin says
this looks
more like
a goat which
proves how
much he
knows.
A goat once
ate his
football
magazine so
he's probably
got them on
the brain.

Look very carefully at these next three. They were difficult and I got cross and said SOD THE COMPUTER and worse, which got me into trouble because our house is supposed to be a NO SWEARING zone.

SLEEPING DRAGON

dragonsdragonsdragonsdragonsZZZgonsdragonsdragonsdragons
dragonsdragonsdragonsdragonZZZagonsdragonsdragonsdragons
dragonsdragonsdragonsdragoZZZragonsdragonsdragonsdragons
dragonsdragonsdragonsdragonZZZagonsdragonsdragonsdragons
dragonsdragonsdragonsdragonsZZZgonsdragonsdragonsdragons
dragonsdragonsdragonsdragonZZZagonsdragonsdragonsdragons
dragonsdragonsdragonsdragoZZZragonsdragonsdragonsdragons
dragonsdragonsdragonsdragonZZZagonsdragonsdragonsdragons
dragonsdragonsdragonsdragonsZZZgonsdragonsdragonsdragons
dragonsdragonsdragonsdragonZZZagonsdragonsdragonsdragons
dragonsdragonsdragonsdragonsZragonsdragonsdragonsdragons
dragonsdragonsdragonsdragonZZZagonsdragonsdragonsdragons
dragonsdragonsdragonsdragonsZZZgonsdragonsdragonsdragons
dragonsdragonsdragonsdragonZZZagonsdragonsdragonsdragons
dragonsdragonsdragonsdragoZZZragonsdragonsdragonsdragons
dragonsdragonsdragonsdragonZZZagonsdragonsdragonsdragons
dragonsdragonsdragonsdragonsZZZgonsdragonsdragonsdragons
dragonsdragonsdragonsdragonZZZagonsdragonsdragonsdragons
dragonsdragonsdragonsdragoZZZragonsdragonsdragonsdragons
dragonsdragonsdragonsdragonZZZagonsdragonsdragonsdragons
dragonsdragonsdragonsdragonsZZZgonsdragonsdragonsdragons
dragonsdragonsdragonsdragonZZZagonsdragonsdragonsdragons
dragonsdragonsdragonsdragoZZZragonsdragonsdragonsdragons
dragonsdragonsdragonsdragonZZZagonsdragonsdragonsdragons

ZZZZZZZZZZZZZZZZZZZZZZZZZZZZZZZZZZZZZZZ
ZZZZZZZZZZZZZZZZZZUMZZZZZZZZZZZZZZZ
ZZZZZZZZZZZZZZZZZZZZZZZZZZZZZZZZZZZZZZZ
ZZZZZZZZZZZZZZZZZZZZZZZZZZZZZZZZZZZZZZZ
ZZZZZZZZZZZZZZZZZZZZZZZZZZZZZZZUMMY
ZZZZZZZZZZZZZZZZZZZZZZZZZZZZZZZZZZZZZZZ
ZZZZZZZZZZZZZZZZZZZZZZZZZZZZZZZZZZZZZZZ
ZZZZZZZZZZZZZZZZZZZZZZZZZZZZZZZZZZZZZZZ
ZZZZZZZZZZZZZZZZZZZZZZZZZZZZZZZZZZZZZZZ
BEAUTIFUZZZZZZZZZZZZZZZZZZZZZCRUMMY
ZZZZZZZZZZZZZZZZZZZZZZZZZZZZZZZZZZZZZZZ
ZZZZZZZZZZZZZZZZZZZZZZZZZZZZZZZZZZZZZZZ
ZZZZZZZZZZZZZZZZZZZZZZZZZZZZZZZZZZZZZZZ
ZZZZZZZZZZZZZZZZZZZZZZZZZZZZZZZZZ
BEAUTIFULLADYSCRUMMYSCRUMMY
ZZZZZZZZZZZZZZZZZZZZZZZZZZZZZZZZZZZZZZZ
ZZZZZZZZZZZZZZZZZZZZZZZZZZZZZZZZZZZZZZZ
ZZZZKNIGHTINARMOURZZZZZZZZZZZZ
ZZZZZZZZZZZZZZZZZZZZCOMINGTOGET-
MECOMINGTOGETMEZZZZZZZZZZZZZZZ
ZZZZZZZZZZZZZZZZZZZZZZZZZZZZZZZZZZZZZZZ
ZZZZZZZZZZZZZZZZZZZZZZZZZZZZZZZZZZZZZZZ
ZZZZZZZZZZZZZZZZZZZZZZZZZZZZZZZZZZZZZZZ
CLUMPCLUMPCLUMPCLUMPIWANTMYMUM-
MYMUMMYMUMMY!(*)&$ú*{?}/\!!aglassofwaterther
etheretheresettledowndeartheretheretheZZZZZZZZZ
ZZZZZZZZZZZZZZZZZZZZZZZZZZZZZZUMUMUM

acrosstheriver&intothetreesa
crosstheriver&intothetreesac
rosstheriver&intothetreesacr
osstheriver&intothetreesacro
sstheriver&intothetreesacros
stheriver&intothetreesacross
theriver&intothetreesacrosst
heriver&intothetreesacrossth
eriver&intothetreesacrossthe
river&intothetreesacrossther
iver&intothetreesacrosstheri
ver&intothetreesacrosstheriv
er&intothetreesacrosstherive
r&intothetreesacrosstheriver
&intothetreesacrosstheriver&
intothetreesacrosstheriver&i
ntothetreesacrosstheriver&in
tothetreesacrosstheriver&int
othetreesacrosstheriver&into
thetreesacrosstheriver&intot
hetreesacrosstheriver&intoth
etreesacrosstheriver&intothe
treesacrosstheriver&intothet
reesacrosstheriver&intothetr
eesdragontheriver&intothetre
esacrosstheriver&intothetree
sacrosstheriver&intothetrees

59

THE CAT SAT ON THE COMPUTER

Mitzi wasn't hurt when the computer fell on her though I suppose she may have used up one of her nine lives. No I don't. I may be Artistic but I know cats have one life just like anybody else.

The cat sat on the computer
It couldn't have been cuter
The cat on the computer

The cat sat on the computer
The cat was our cat Mitzi
And she sitzi where she wants to sitzi

The cat sat on the computer
The computer was an Amstrad
The Amstrad of my dad

The cat sat on the computer
The computer swayed like a tree
And the cat sat there contentedly

The cat sat on the computer
One day there was a crash
One day there was a smash

And the computer sat on the cat

GOING FOR EUROPE

I'm not a horrid Euro-phobe. I'm up to the minute and international and I've been to France. I've even been up the Eiffel Tower, or 'La Tour Eiffel', as they say over there. I can also say French things like 'J'adore les pop-groups' and 'Je deteste le Channel-Ferry'. So this poem 'est une blague'. A joke, don't you know?

> They're not like BRITISH human beans –
> Each one's a bandit and a cheater!
> I mean those dodgy Euro-peans –
> Give them an inch and they'll take 0.9142857 of a metre.

CROSS CHANNEL

There are lots of problems about France, like French ALL THE TIME and funny money and crossing the road. But the worst problem is getting there. Did you know we were joined on to France in the time of the dinosaurs?

> You don't want to cross the Channel
> in a ferry with a funnel
> or to lean against a gunwale
> feeling blue

while your tummy sort of bunches
and it gloops and grunts and scrunches
and your breakfast or your lunch is
turned to goo

so you take a pill and suck it
(there's a packet in your pocket)
then you stagger to a bucket
in the loo

and you feel an utter pillock
for you're sicker than a parrot
with the yoghurt and the carrot
and the stew

so you huddle
hugger-mugger
in the toilet
(very flooded)
with a flannel
on your forehead
and you're feeling
mega-horrid
as you paddle
in a puddle
and your tummy's
in a muddle
and you need
a Mummy-cuddle

on the ferry
with a funnel
in the middle
of the Channel
oh you wish
you'd gone by tunnel

YES YOU DO!

THE TROUBLE WITH GRANDAD

Our grandad has a football scarf
And woolly football hat.
He likes to sing the football songs
And chat the football chat.
He likes to cheer the football cheer
And drink the football lager beer.

Six days a week and he's OK,
A well-behaved old thing.
But on the football Saturday
It's so embarrassing,
A quiet, silver-haired old man
Behaving like a football fan.

He stamps and yells and (oh the shame)
He's even got a rattle.
I tell him how it's just a game.
He acts like it's a battle.
ARSENAL! ARSENAL FOR THE CUP!
Do grandads ever quite grow up?

It isn't me who goes, it's Justin. And nothing
embarrasses him. He tells me it isn't Arsenal –
only sad people support Arsenal – it's Tottenham
Hotspur. That sounds more like a recipe to me. I
like Sheffield Wednesday. If Manchester United
were Manchester Friday, then they wouldn't be
Man United, they'd be... Oh forget it.

WHAT IS IT?

This is a Riddle. Find the answer on page 116.

What is it?
You won't find it in writing,
Or fighting or biting,
A small thing.
What is it?

Usually you don't think about it.

But today
I took it away
Skilfully, thoroughly, fas-tid-i-ous-ly,
I took it RIGHT OUT.

Now you must think about it.
Now you must look for it.

(Watch out!
It's not about!)

Look at this word –

Floccinaucinihilipilification.

A frabjous word!
Wham! Bam! Alakazam!
A most gy-normous word
I found it in my dictionary.

65

If you say,
'That isn't worth much in my opinion,'
This is

Floccinaucinihilipilification.

Got it?

But what I'm talking about
Isn't in that word at all.
Oh No! Not at all!
Long as that word is.

What is it?

THE LONGEST WORD

It wouldn't fit into the last poem, and besides, I think it deserves a poem of its own. It sounds horrid and I hope I never get it. I'm sure you will notice that the poem is a triolet. This is a poetry book that TEACHES you things.

Pneumonoultramicroscopicsilicovolcanoconiosis
Is a disease of the lungs.
It gets in up people's noses
Pneumonoultramicroscopicsilicovolcanoconiosis
They don't get it in toeses.
They don't get it in tongues.
Pneumonoultramicroscopicsilicovolcanoconiosis
Is a disease of the lungs.

HAIKU

A haiku is very short and Japanese. The way you write a haiku (pronounced Hi coo! as if you were talking to a scottish cow) is to write a line of five syllables, then one of seven syllables, then one of five syllables, then stop and give it a title. Like this.

TIDDLY-POM HAIKU

tiddly pom tiddly
pom tiddly pom tiddly pom
tiddly pom tiddly

Here's mine which is true. The other cat is Sholto the bird-killer. He is Mitzi's brother and they've had eight kittens together. This is all right in the cat world and also if you are an Egyptian Pharaoh.

CAT AND MOUSE HAIKU

two purry cats on
my duvet this morning – dead
mouse in my knickers

WHY DO THEY ALWAYS PLAY AT KISS-CHASE IN THE INFANTS' PLAYGROUND?

This is Emma's poem. She said it to me. I had to rearrange it of course. People don't go about saying haikus. Very short poems often have very long titles, though it's not a rule.

> don't like kissing boys
> would very much prefer to
> go bungy-jumping

PETS

Ursula Veitch has probably the most interesting pet. It's an iguana, but she particularly doesn't want it talked about. I don't believe in Emma's pen-friend's python.

> Emily Hogg
> has got a dog
> (a Red Setter)
>
> Stephen Pratt
> has got a cat
> (not any kind in particular)
>
> Harry Heep
> has got a sheep
> (on his uncle's farm he said)

Moira Murbles
has got three gerbils
(plus one gone under the shed)

Randy Rootes
has got five newts
(which you can't quite count now the pond's gone green)

Polly Pointdex-
ter has got absolutely trillions of red-kneed stick insex
(truthfully fourteen)

But Daniel Jerrit
freckly Daniel Jerrit
red-haired knobbly Daniel Jerrit
has got

the sweetest
the darlingest
the cuddliest
the kindest

POLECAT FERRET
(which he actually takes for walks on a ferret lead)

DRAGONS FRAGMENT

I am definitely into dragons. This only uses the letters of 'dragons', and was composed on the fridge door, replacing 'phoebe is a fat pig true' which is Justin's pathetic idea of wit.

ago ago ago
song sang
ago ago ago
sad o sad
gods sang ago
sang sad gods
sand sand sand
ago ago ago
sang and sang ago
ago ago ago
sang on and on and on
sad and sand and sad and sand
gongongongongon
gon...

My pet dragon ←

Me ↗

CHRISTMAS CAROL

Every word of this is true though it did happen a bit ago. Now we are older we do World Peace and Ecology. I'm being a dolphin, which is a bit wet – ha, ha.

Come to our Nativity Play,
Raggy doll asleep on the hay,
Itchy knickers, bogey-pickers,
I've got a bit to say.
O, I'm the star as you can tell.
I'm the Angel Gabriel.
Silver wings and halo thing and
Glittery tights as well.

They two kings of Orient are
Kevin Jones and Dominic Barr.
Barry Bright has tonsilitis –
Sick in his father's car.
O, I'm the star etc.

See the shepherds watching their sheep.
Amber Cardy's gone off to sleep.
I saw her snogging Nathaniel Hogg in the
Cloakrooms and he's a creep!
O, I'm the star etc.

Mary, Mary, good as can be,
Thinks she's always better than me,
Till my candle burns her sandal

71

Quite accidentally.
O, I'm the star etc.

Adam's Herod, up on a chair
In his robe and underwear.
It's so rude, he's nearly NUDE
And I saw his pants, so there.
O, I'm the star etc.

Vivian and Julius King,
Back and front of camel thing.
They just fight, it isn't right,
And so embarrassing.
O, I'm the star etc.

Mums and Grandmas sit in a row,
Toddlers want to be in the show,
Dads who are able to stand on a table to
Get it on video.
O I'm the star etc.

CHRISTMAS CAROL TWO

Did you know that the Pope wears Doc Martens?

When first Noel
Was eating his lunch
And Jane sat down beside him
He gave her a punch.
Jane shoved Noel

When Noel punched Jane
Then she called him a pig and
She punched him again.
Noel, Noel, Noel, Noel,
You're as thick as a brick
And you're fat and you smell.

Noel, Noel,
Said Mrs McHugh,
You mustn't hit Jane when
She's smaller than you.
So Noel stamped
Jane's crisps in the dirt
And Jane poured her orange juice
Right down his shirt.
Noel, Noel, etc.

When Noel stuck
His thumb up her nose
Jane stamped her Doc Martens
All over his toes.
So Noel snapped
Jane's new Alice Band
And Jane LOST HER TEMPER
And bit Noel's hand.
Noel, Noel, etc.

Noel thought that
Was not very fair
And emptied his yoghurt pot
Over her hair

Noel, Noel,
Said the Deputy Head,
It's the Season of Joy
Not of Fighting, she said.
Noel, Noel, etc.

She started it Miss.
She said something bad
When she said Father Christmas
Was really our Dad.
And how can that
Be possibly true
When Dad lives in Glasgow
With our Auntie Pru?
Noel, Noel, etc.

FIRST LIMERICK

Holy people get into limericks all the time. Them
and camels. Most limericks are VERY RUDE and
you can't write them down in this sort of book.
But this one's OK.

Auntie Flick was so sick at the vicar's.
She was sick in her best party knickers
Which she'd just taken off
To cover a cough –
She's jolly polite, Auntie Flick is.

74

SCRABBLE LIMERICK

Mum is so useless at Scrabble it's quite shaming.
She puts down words like REALISE and
SOLUTION and TRILLIONS when she should be
looking for AX and JOB and QUIZ because Q
and Z and J and X are the high-scoring letters.
This poem may help her. (AX is often spelled like
that in Scrabble though not in real life.) If you
can do a higher-scoring limerick you can write it
in here instead.

A Judge and a sQuaw and a piXie
RelaXed to a Juke boX in diXie.
They JiVed eXtra JaZZily,
RaZZamataZZily,
Then Jumped in a taXi Quite Quick, see.

THIRD LIMERICK

To get this one right you have to know that posh
people pronounce the name St John in a daft
way like you were burning or something. I also
know that Apache and Sioux are Native
Americans, but that doesn't rhyme.

Lord Jolyon Montgomery St John
Liked to dress himself up as an t John
But his hyioux was too flache

75

For Sioux or Apache
If you want my humble oPt John.

UR LIMERICK

My dad never can understand why we like going to Sunday School when he always hated it. But he doesn't know that modern Sunday School is mostly sticking in and cutting out which is a lot better than going back to Sainsbury's for what we forgot on Saturday. Anyway, that's where we learned about Ur. It had a thing called a ziggurat in the middle but I couldn't get that in.

There once was a city called UR
Though the where and the when are a blur,
And perhaps there were some
Called YUK, EEK and UM
Round about. Yes I'm sure that there were.

STOP PRESS. It was going round and round in my mind while I was supposed to be doing Topic and Miss Hornbeam was quite rude when I said it was Henry the Sixth who had eight wives. But I've got it. (It was the man from St Ives who had eight wives wasn't it?

SECOND UR LIMERICK

They built it both better and bigger at
UR. Yes they did. Can you figure it?
A lop-sided pyramid.
I've drawn one right here amid
Acres of sand. It's a...
      ZIGGURAT!

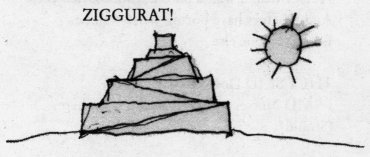

DOCTORS AND NURSES

I wrote this when I was younger. I'm older and wiser now. Doctors and nurses save lives. (Not the school one, who's useless). But the future of the human race lies in the hands of us poets.

I wanted to be a nurse
THEY SAID why not be a doctor
I SAID girls don't get to be doctors
THEY SAID yours did (which is true)
I still wanted to be a nurse
Doctors don't get to wear the hats
Only boring white coats like in supermarkets

THEY SAID Doctors can listen to people's hearts
With those you know stethy things
I SAID nice doctors would let nurses do it
I bet ours would (she's nice)

I still wanted to be a nurse
Nurses wear a watch on the front of their dress
And Doctors have boring wrist-watches
Like everyone else

THEY SAID Doctors have bags
I SAID Nurses can have bags too so there
(Stupid)

But I want to be a Doctor now
Nurses don't get to cut people up

Actually, I don't want to have anything to do with doctors anymore since the injection when I fainted. It was very hot in the room and I hadn't had breakfast due to Justin my brother doing See-Food.

SHOES OFF

Mum's not at all bossy compared to some, but she does have a thing about shoes. She says we'll all get tidy when we are older but it doesn't seem to have happened to Dad. Mum says it's because he's a man, which is obviously a sexist remark.

Mum says to Emma (Quiet as any mouse)
'Darling, take your shoes off
In the house.'

Mum says to me next (Speaking very nice)
'Did you take your shoes off, dear?
I've asked you twice.'

Mum says to Justin (Now she's getting cross)
'Take your rotten shoes off if
You know who's boss.'

Hi Dad! Hi Dad! (He's stomping up our street)
Hi kids! Whaddyadoing?
                Shhh!
We're watching feet.

We're watching feet (And we're still as still)
Dad'll take his shoes off
Dad'll take his shoes off
Dad'll take his shoes off...

COURSE HE WILL!

THE BLOAT FILES

Continued from page 51

The story so far: Horace Bloat is rich but he isn't happy. He starts a wish and an old lady appears at his door. He thinks she is his Fairy Godmother. Now read on:

Chapter Two

Get real! You must know that rich men don't have fairy-godmothers.

The sweet old lady shook her head, 'I'm Mrs Penge, dearie.'

'But who are you?' cried Horace, mystified.

'I'm your daily person. Nobody never notices the likes of me.' She clanked her bucket and shook her mop as she spoke.

'What shall I do, Mrs Penge?' cried Horace. 'I've got all this money but I'm not happy.'

'Give it away, ducks,' said Mrs Penge, after a pause for thought. 'Money doesn't buy you happiness. Could you move that guitar? I need to do in here.'

'Give it away!' said Horace. 'Why didn't I think of that?'

'Two heads are better than one, dearie,' said Mrs Penge, who was old and wise and therefore knew a lot of stuff like that.

Horace sprang to his feet. '*You* have the money, Mrs Penge. You have it all. Let me write the cheque out here and now.'

There and then he wrote her a personal cheque for £4,722,311,948.25p.

'Luvaduck,' said Mrs Penge. 'I think I'll just have a sit down. Could you put your kettle on. My kettle,' she corrected herself.

She was going to say, 'A fool and his money are soon parted,' but then she thought she wouldn't.

Continued on page 108

NATURE

Grown-ups are very keen on Nature Poetry. This is because the only poems they know are this one:

De-dum-de-dum-de dum-de-dum
De-dum-de-dum-de-dum-de-dum
De-dum-de-dum-de daffodils.

which is by William Wordsworth, and this one:

De-dum-de-dum-de-dum-de-dum
De-dum-de-dum-de-dum-de-dum
Stands the church clock at ten to three
And is there honey still for tea?

... which isn't. By William Wordsworth I mean. You will notice I've got honey for tea into my poem. This is allowed because the poet's been dead for a long time. You can't pinch my poetic things because I haven't been dead.

82

DO-IT-YOURSELF NATURE POEM

Autumn

De-dum-de-dum-de leaves of brown
De-dum-de-dum-de fluttering down
De-dum-de-dum-de-dum-de conkers
De-dum-de-dum-de-dum-de bonkers

killer bee

Winter

De-dum-de-dum-de in the snow
De-dum-de-dum-de sledges go
De-dum-de-dum-de ice and sleet
De-dum-de-dum-de freezing feet

Spring

De-dum-de-dum-de crocus flowers
De-dum-de-dum-de April showers
De-dum-de-dum-de squelchy smelly
De-dum-de-dum-de slug in welly

daffodils

Summer

De-dum-de-dum-de cricket bats
De-dum-de-dum-de floppy hats
De-dum-de-dum-de honey teas
De-dum-de savage killer bees

ADAM ATE A BEETLE

I believe insects are very nutritious and I ate garlicky snails in Calais on a day trip. They are actually very nice and you eat them with a cute little instrument. Somebody told me that in China they eat chocolate-coated ants but that's hard to believe.

Adam ate a beetle
Did it for a dare, Miss

A big black beetle
Found it on his chair, Miss

A horrid squashy beetle
Put it in my hair, Miss

A dear little beetle
And he doesn't even care, Miss

(Pigface, I never)

Oooh what a rotten lie
Don't go spare, Miss

What a massive porky-pie
I swear, Miss

Shall I tell you why
I was there, Miss?

Cross my throat and wish to die
My dare, Miss

(I think I'm going to be sick)

SWEET

When Stefanie sees a fly
She says,
    'How sweet
Your sixty-four sweet eyes
And your six sweet feet!
Fly, you're an icky-picky poo.
Fly, you're so sweet I shall call you Fred!'

I can't imagine a more boring name, can you?
Fly, show your ugly mug round here – you're dead.

There is nothing sweet about flies.
They carry disease and dirt.
In fact the surprise is,
The one good thing about flies is,
They are food for Bert.

Bert is my pet spider
And she is extremely sweet.

Of course flies have as much right to exist in the Universe as humans do. But there is no need to go over the top about it.

DREAM POEM

This was my dream. Jessica, who is into
psychology, says it is an anxiety dream and that I
am anxious about very large insects. I once got
stung by a wasp and I am definitely allergic.

I dream a dream about a door
Into the dream I dreamed before.
I turn the key, I push, and then
I see the garden once again.
The waking world around me seems
Much less real than my dreams.

I dream a dream about a child
Who plays within the garden wild,
Where bracken grows as tall as trees
And creaks in every summer breeze,
Where grasses sighing brush your face.
There are no people in the place.

But there beneath gigantic roses,
Worms as fat as garden hoses,
Beetles anoraked in steel,
Snails the size of tractor wheels,
Slugs like hoover bags gone wrong,
Millipedes a metre long.

Bees in burglars' jerseys whirr
Like chain-saws through that atmosphere.
Butterflies have alien faces
And wings the size of pillow-cases.
Pumpkin-plump, a spider waits
Beside her silver fishing nets.

I dream a pond where fishes rise
Making mouths at Paradise.
I dream a tower by the pond
And, from the top, the views beyond
The wall spread out like coloured maps
To... where? I do not know. Perhaps

I'll climb the tower. Perhaps. I may
Tomorrow. I may not. Today
I know I do not care to care.
I watch the spider in her lair.
I watch her watch the butterfly
Who finds too soon the way to die.

MR ALUCARD

Do you know Mr Alucard?
His handshake is as soft as lard,
The pallid Mr Alucard.

Do you know Mr Alucard?
His handshake is as soft as lard,
His eyes are sad, his cheeks are scarred,
Romantic Mr Alucard.

Do you know Mr Alucard?
His handshake is as soft as lard,
His eyes are sad, his face is scarred,
His breath is aromatic nard,
Sweet-smelling Mr Alucard.

Do you know Mr Alucard?
His handshake is as soft as lard,
His eyes are sad, his cheeks are scarred,
His breath is aromatic nard,
He takes a midnight promenade,
Nocturnal Mr Alucard.

Do you know Mr Alucard?
His handshake is as soft as lard,
His eyes are sad, his cheeks are scarred,
His breath is aromatic nard,
He takes a midnight promenade,
When velvet skies are diamond starred,
Mysterious Mr Alucard.

Do you know Mr Alucard?
His handshake is as soft as lard,
His eyes are sad, his cheeks are scarred,
His breath is aromatic nard,
He takes a midnight promenade,
When velvet skies are diamond starred,
Among the graves in chapelyard,
Sepulchral Mr Alucard.

Do you know Mr Alucard?
His handshake is as soft as lard,
His eyes are sad, his cheeks are scarred,
His breath is aromatic nard,
He takes a midnight promenade,
When velvet skies are diamond starred,
Among the graves in chapelyard,
Fabulous as Scheherazade,
You MUST know Mr Alucard.

Yes I know Mr Alucard
Whose handshake is as soft as lard,
Whose eyes are sad, whose cheeks are scarred,
Whose breath is aromatic nard,
Who takes a midnight promenade,
When velvet skies are diamond starred,
Among the graves in chapelyard,
Fabulous as Scheherazade...
We know him by his calling card,
The cryptic Mr Alucard.

```
A L U C A R D
L L U C A R R
U U U C A A A
C C C C C C C
A A A C U U U
R R A C U L L
D R A C U L A
```

Adam Burke says what's 'nard' anyway and he
doesn't like show-offs who use words nobody can
understand. But if I only used words he could
understand I'd be stuck at the Mr Men books.
Nard is in the dictionary.

OLD MACDONALD HAD A ZOO

This one is a bit silly but everyone should be silly for ten minutes each day. Some are already of course. Adam Burke is very silly indeed.

The sheep goes baa
And the cow goes moo
The budgie goes twit
And the owl goes twoo

The corncrake crakes
In the craking corn
And the three-toed sloth goes
YAAAAAAAAAAAAAWN

The cuck goes oo
And the buzz goes bee
The laughing hyena goes
He he he

The laughing hyena goes
Ho ho ho
The rook goes rook
And the crow goes crow

The whale goes cluck
And the quack goes baa
Sucky-sucky-suck goes
Dracula

Dracula goes
Sucky-sucky-suck
Ha ha ha goes
The laughing duck

And the crying shame goes
boo-hoo-hoo
And the highland cow goes
coo

And the chiff goes chaff
And the kit goes kat
And the wasp in the jam goes
Slurp slurp **SPLAT**

DO-IT-YOURSELF INSULT POEM

One of the reasons to write poems is **TO GET YOUR OWN BACK.** This one works! They sang it in the Infants' playground for **THREE** days.

Adam Burke is very dumb,
He's got a face like an elephant's bum.

You can use it too if you have a problem with someone whom makes Uncalled-for Personal Remarks. It will be your poem because you can slot in the personalised bits. Poets often do it.

Adam Burke
Lady MacBeth
Attila the Hun
The Referee
The bitey dog two doors down } is very dumb.
Mrs Bird (the horrid dinner lady)
Whoever stole the Kit-Kat out of my lunch box
Catherine The Great Empress Of All The Russias
Madonna (this is a purely personal opinion)

He
She's got a face like a(n) { elephant / butterfly / pterodactyl / baboon / three-toed sloth / alien from Betelgeuse / tarantula / headmaster / palmated newt } 's bum.
It

HEADLINES

I got some of these out of a book by Fritz Spiegl. He got them from newspapers. Thank you, Mr Spiegl. I'm not really getting old. It's just there for the rhyme.

It's the headlines make me stare.

MEGASTAR WALKS OUT ON AIR

It's the headlines stop me dead.

PUBLIC BODY NEEDS NEW HEAD

Have you seen the things they say?

CHANNEL TUNNEL TALKS TODAY

Some of them are hard to beat.

SPOTTED MAN IN LONDON STREET

Some are definitely chilling.

SUSPECTS HELD FOR HEAVY GRILLING

Some would make your toenails curl.

BOY SUSPENDED OVER GIRL

Some are more or less OK.

MORE PUBLIC TOILETS WATCHDOGS SAY

Some are absolutely barmy.

FRENCH PUSH BOTTLES UP GERMAN ARMY

Now I fear I'm getting old.

NUDISTS ALL LEFT OUT IN COLD

And those headlines make me older.

ANGRY CHEF HAS CHIP ON SHOULDER

If my mind was sharp not blunt,

GENERAL FLIES BACK TO FRONT

Making sense of gibberish,

MINISTER STANDS FIRM ON FISH

Then my brain would function quicker.

DO YOU WANT A WOMAN VICAR?

GRANNY SONG

I would like to say that my real granny is not like this at all. She's totally perfect, most particularly when my birthday comes up. Did you hear that, Granny? What I'd like is a Pentium Processor and I can go and choose it. But I don't suppose the Old Age Pension goes that far. Never mind, Granny. I love you for yourself. This is only a poem, not real at all.

I'm going to do for Granny.
I'll bash her with a brick,
Or feed her deadly nightshade,
Or arsenic,
Or fill her bath with acid,
Or dynamite her bed,
Or drop her in the river
Wearing boots of lead.

She doesn't look like grannies look
Or act like grannies act.
She's got no trace of granniness
And that's a fact.
Most other people's grannies
Are silver-haired and small,
My granny is a skin'ead
And she's six feet tall.

Most other people's grannies
Wear clothes all dull and old.
My granny wears a cat-suit
Made of solid gold.
And other people's grannies
Have warts and piles and bunions.
My granny's piles are diamonds
As big as pickled onions.

Some grannies' teeth come out at night.
They keep them in a jar.
My granny's got great gleaming fangs
Like Dracula.
Other grannies sip their cocoa
Or tea or chicken soup.
My granny swigs Jamaica Rum.
Glub-glub-gloop.

Some grannies like milk pudding
In a special little dish.
But my granny crunches chillis
And piranha fish.
Other grannies get their pensions
And pay them to the bank
That my Granny robs at lunchtime
With a Sherman Tank.

Some grannies do the shopping
In a little batricar.
My granny sends her toy boy
On his Yamaha.
And when the other grannies
Sit on benches in the park
My granny and her toy boy
Go and fish for shark.

So I'm going to do for Granny.
I'll bash her with a club
As soon as she and toy boy
Stagger out the pub.
I'll zap her with a zapper.
I'll shoot her with a gun.
It's far too good, this grannihood.
It's too much FUN!

Granny says I am a miserable
little toad.

BORING

I didn't write the first two lines of this one. I heard them from my friend Jessica. You can hear poetry every day if you just listen.

I'm dead bored
 bored to the bone.
Nobody likes me.
 I'm all alone.
I'll just go crawl
 under a stone.

Hate my family,
 got no friends.
I'll sit here till
 the Universe ends
Or I starve to death.
 It all depends.

Then I'll be dead,
 dead and rotten,
Less than a blot that's
 been well blotten,
Less than a teddy bear
 that's been forgotten.

Then I'll go to heaven which is
 more than can be said

For certain persons
 when they're dead
They'll go you-know-
 where instead.

Then they'll be sorry,
 then they'll be glum,
Sitting on a stove till
 kingdom come.
They can all go
 kiss my bum.

Bum's a sort of swearing.
 People shouldn't swear.
I won't go to heaven but
 I don't care.
 I don't care.
 I don't care.
I'll sit here and swear.
                    So there!

Except that it's boring!

This is what Emma said to her best friend Tamsin.
I really just wrote it down. That makes it a
Found Poem, like an interesting pebble or a
bone you see just lying about and take home.

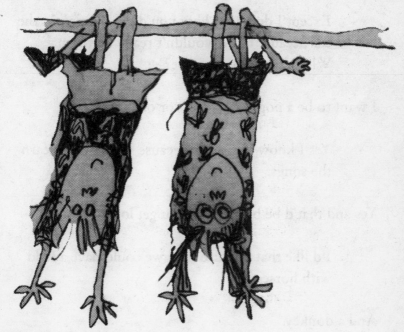

What do you want to be?

    I want to be a hairdresser.

You don't want to be one of those.

    Why not?

Because you have to work in a shop and you have to go there and be there and you wouldn't like that.

> I'd be one of those that goes round to people's houses like Sharon's mum.

That'd be nice.

> Except I don't see how you'd get the sink in the car because there wouldn't really be room.
> What do you want to be?

I want to be a pop star except for one thing.

> Yes I know what it is because you have to learn the songs.

Yes and that'd be boring but you get lots of money.

> I'd like that because then we could have a field with horses in it.

And a donkey.

> Yes and a donkey.

INVISIBLES

This is another thing I heard. I also heard Adam
Burke say he was a pit bull terrier when he bit
Daniel Jerrit but I haven't made a poem about it
because Adam Burke would get big-headed if I
kept putting him in poems and might think I
FANCIED him which is utterly ridiculous. Also,
he's an Aries and you can't trust them.

We have invisibles and they live in an orphanage and
we need to be very rich because
there are 6,045 of them in the orphanage and
in charge of them are me
as well as Karen and Chantelle and Stef and
Jonathan when he feels like it and Idris and

the orphanage is lit by candlelight because
me and Karen think that is more cosy but
Idris is modern with trains and stuff and
he built an extension and in the extension
are all the electric things like
lights and kettles and radiators and
radios and televisions and videos and mixers and

to tell the truth me and Karen
have moved to an orphanage of our own because
6,045 is a lot of invisibles to manage and
we don't like Idris's modern electricity because
of harming the environment and because
old-fashioned candlelight is definitely more cosy.

The orphanage is that white wall over there.

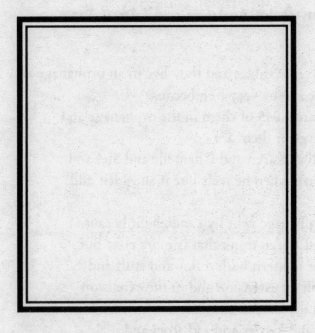

A picture of an invisible

POSITIVELY THE LAST POEM ABOUT DRAGONS

I don't believe all that St George stuff about
dragons eating maidens and ruining the country-
side. It sounds like foxhunters saying foxes eat
babies. Or is it rats that eat babies? It's more likely
to be babies that eat rats, the babies you see about.

Dragons are the gentlest creatures,
We just want to come and meet yers,
We would never want to eat yers.
DRAGONS!

Airy 'uns, fairy 'uns, ever-so-slightly scary 'uns,
Huge high hairy 'uns, none of us are barbarians,
All of us are strictly vegetarians.
DRAGONS!

Dancing dragons shake a leg for you,
We will even sit and beg for you,
And our breath will boil and egg for you,
DRAGONS!

Loch Ness dragons love a ceilidh,
Squeeze your dragon, squeeze him daily,
Though his hide is rough and scaly,
DRAGONS!

Shout out loud, don't put a gag on,
Strut on, stroll on, boast on, brag on,
Raise your glass and raise your flagon,
DRAGONS!

TEN ANSWERS
to the quiz on page 38

These answers have been carefully researched by me asking anyone I could think of and making up the other bits. Adam Burke says they're all on CD-ROM but I'm artistic and the pig won't do it for me.

1. I'll tell you that when you tell me what sort of an animal Goofy is supposed to be.

2. This is because you nearly always lose the right hand glove, don't you? And that's because you take it off more often to do things.

3. I don't know but some printing machines say ETAOINSHRDLU and do you know why that is? It is because they are the commonest letters in English in order. It's quite easy to remember if you say it like two words.

       ETAOIN SHRDLU
       ALL IN A MDLU
       IN A BIG PDLU
       NEEDED A CDLU

4. It *is* itchy on sheep. They scratch all the time, poor things.

5. It's a brush-for-teeth in French, did you know?

6. Emma says you can be what age you like but do you grow up?

7. Why do your nails grow but not your teeth? Elephants' teeth do grow.

8. According to Karen (whose mum's a vicar) Saints don't get them till after they're dead. But what about Jesus then? And why doesn't God have one? Karen's mum's working on it.

9. My dad says it's to do with the curve of the earth but I don't understand how.

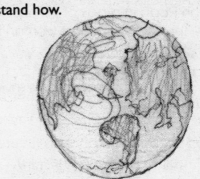

10. People also think Sharon Teakle saying 'thixty-thix' when she means 'sixty-six' is sweet and juniors still supposing Santa Claus comes down chimneys (how dirty he'd get for a start), that is sweet too. People are dumb, obviously.

THE BLOAT FILES

Continued from page 81

The story so far: Horace Bloat was once fabulously rich but he has rashly given all his money away to his daily cleaning woman, Mrs Penge. Now read on:

Chapter Three

A very little later and Horace Bloat was walking down the High Road in a pair of painty overalls that Mrs Penge, the second-richest woman in England, had kindly given him.

He had his guitar slung over his shoulder (Mrs Penge couldn't play).

He had £1.50p in his pockets (interest earned in the time it took to write the cheque).

He felt totally happy for the first time in his life. He felt free. He called in at Mr Jumadeen the newsagent and spent 50p on four ounces of sherbet lemons. (That's 113.5 grammes in nasty Euroweights.)

With the pound he bought a Lottery ticket, a fun thing he had never done before.

'I'll have myself a flutter,' he thought to himself, 'just like poor people.'

'It's a double rollover week,' said Mr Jumadeen, smiling as he weighed out the sherbet lemons. 'Fill in your six numbers on the form, sir. Perhaps this week it's you.'

'But which six numbers shall I choose?' said Horace, chewing his fingers. 'I don't know how to do this.' Then he remembered.

47 22 31 19 48 25. The figures had stuck in his mind. He wrote them down quickly and handed his form to Mr Jumadeen.

On Saturday, at his Auntie Pam's Bed & Breakfast in Ponder's End (he had to stay with his auntie because he had no money now), Horace Bloat watched the National Lottery Show.

Mystic Meg predicted the winner had recently changed his or her life. Horace was excited. The balls bounced ...

ZUNK! One of the new privatised power cuts. As he sat in the dark and Auntie Pam looked round for the candles, Horace wondered what the winning numbers would turn out to be. He had a funny feeling in his bones.

Continued on page 124

THE COLLECTOR

This is what is called a List poem. You can make them very long. My 'What Is Wrong With Adam Burke Poem' goes on for a hundred and twenty-seven lines but he's not having TWO poems about him in one book.

I collect stuff
 but not everything

I don't collect stamps
 penny blacks and cape triangulars

I don't collect coins
 spanish doubloons and silver threepennies

I don't collect pictures
 Rembrandts and footballers

I don't collect tropical fish
 angels and neon tetras

I don't collect fossils
 trilobites and coelocanths

I collect stuff
 but not everything

I collect paperclips
and make them into chains and hang them on my
nose

I collect pencil sharpenings
and crumble them between my fingers

I collect pencil leads
and bash them to powder with my yoghurt
spoon

I collect the ring things
that come off the tops of Lilt and Pepsi cans

I collect bits of rubber
that Daniel Jerrit bites off

I put them in the ink hole of my desk
stirring from time to time

I am a collector
a connoisseur of bric-a-brac

And I also collect
The shrunken heads of my enemies

Plays in poetry are called Verse Plays. They are usually about what happened a long time ago and are Educational. Shakespeare wrote this kind. Dramatis Personae means the people. It's Latin like a.m. and AD and bus. I bet you didn't know bus was Latin. I'm not just a pretty face.

Dramatis Personae

God	The Snake
Adam	The Angel
Eve	The Apple (a non-speaking part)

[God, Adam and Eve come in]

GOD
I told you not to eat the fru-it
But you knew better. You would do it.

ADAM
I didn't want to eat it, Boss.
I said to her that you'd be cross.

EVE
I had a teeny-weeny bite.
The Snake said it would be all right.

GOD
What Snake? I never made a Snake.
I think the Snake is a mistake.

Snow White had problems with apples, too!

THE SNAKE *[whispering]*
Oh yes you did!

GOD
No I did not!

THE SNAKE *[whispering]*
You just conveniently forgot.

ADAM
I told her so, Omnipotence.
But she's a girl. She's got no sense.

EVE
You told me so! You listen, ducky!
What's that, all slithery and yucky?

GOD
The fact remains you disobeyed me.
You've no idea how sad you've made me.
[God goes out]

ADAM
Things are so horrid when he's sad.
See what you get for being bad!

EVE
That's right! Blame me, you little creep.
Your face reminds me of a sheep.

[The Angel comes in, dressed as a policeman]

THE ANGEL
Come on, you little toe-rags! Scoot!

The Owner says he'll prosecute.

ADAM AND EVE *[together]*
We don't think it is very nice
To throw us out of Paradise.

ADAM
It isn't right. It isn't fair.

EVE
I haven't got a thing to wear.

[They all go out except The Snake]

THE SNAKE
    This story's very sad. You know
        I think it only goes to show.
            Don't eat the fruit straight off the trees.
            It could be riddled with disease.
            Don't disobey a Grown-up who
          Can make things very bad for you.
          And lastly, never, never take
         An apple from a talking snake.

[Curtain]

SHAKESPEARE COULDN'T

It seems silly to make such a fuss about a little thing like spelling when all word processors have a spellcheck anyway.

When we have a spelling test
I am not among the best.
At the bottom, truth to tell.
WILLIAM SHAKESPEARE couldn't spell.

I'm not stupid. I'm not thick.
I can do arithmetic,
Very mathematical.
WILLYUM SHAIKSPERE couldn't spell.

I can draw an elephant
(And there's lots of people can't).
I can paint a cockleshell.
WYLLIM SHAIKSPEER couldn't spell.

I am brave and I am tough.
I can do the sporty stuff –
Run and jump like a gazelle.
WILLERM SHAYCKSPURR couldn't spell.

I like drama. I can act.
I'm a genius – that's a fact.
I can sing and dance as well.
WYLM SHAXSPYR cuddernt spel.

TONITE
GLOBE THEETER
HAMLITT

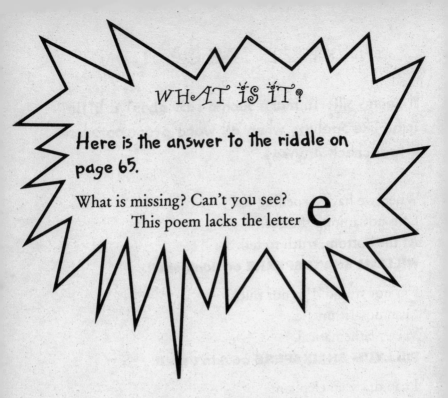

WHAT IS IT?

Here is the answer to the riddle on page 65.

What is missing? Can't you see?
This poem lacks the letter e

MORE 4x4x4x4

I'm sorry to come back to this but there's no getting away from it in our house. Justin goes about slamming doors and muttering. You can't get in the bathroom because he's SHAVING (har har) and there's country flowers talcum powder in whiffy little snowdrifts by the skirting boards.

Valentine's Day
Justin got a
bulgy pink heart
like a teddy's

cushion and (so
em-bar-rass-ing
he has no shame)
he sent this one

ROSES ARE RED
VIOLETS ARE BLUE
I FEEL SEXY
HOW ABOUT YOU?

disgusting eh?
I know because
I steamed open
the envelope

Emma says she
saw Justin and
Banana Boot
(what she calls her)

on our settee
snogging not just
kissing they were
snogging you know

TONGUES (yuk!) I say
Emma what would
you do if for
instance Thomas

Humble tried that?
um says Emma
I'd ask when he
brushed his teeth last

hot news-flash! the
Banana and
my brother have
just BROKEN UP

she sent back tr
lo (half of their
true love ring) and
all his letters

(three including
the disgusting
Valentine) and
his football boots

ah says Emma
boots from the Boot
who gave him the
boot (quite funny)

Eric Gossage
went to GETCHA-
SKATES-ON with the
Hot Banana

and Justin came
home yesterday
with a nose bleed
Eric Gossage

is off school har-
har and you don't
have to be your
actual Sherlock

Holmes to crack it
poor old Justin
what a cow eh
poor old Justin

This is another poem done with the letters on the fridge door. You need a lot of 'n's for this poem. but you can turn the 'u's upside-down, can't you?

THE LONELINESS
FRIDGE POEM

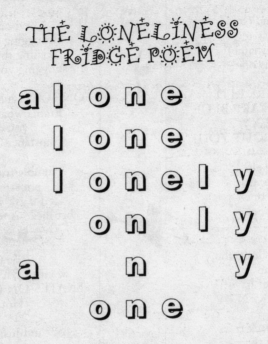

```
al one
 l  one
 l  onely
    on ly
 a    n    y
    one
```

THE CHEER-UP SONG

When you feel got at you need a song like this.
I sing it on my way to school. To myself. I don't
want people staring at me as if I was loopy.

No one likes a boaster
And I'm not one to boast,
But everyone who knows me knows that
I'm the most.

I'm the most attractive, I'm
The Media Superstar,
One hundred per cent in-tell-i-gent
And pop-u-lar.

All my jokes are funny.
Every one's a laugh.
Madonna pays me money for
My au-to-graph.

For I'm the snake's pyjamas, I'm
The bumble-bee's patella,
I'm a juicesome peach at a picnic on the beach, I'm
The rainmaker's umbrella.

Yes I'm the death-by-chocolate, I'm
The curried beans on toast,
And everyone who knows me knows that
I'm the most.

Tee-arr-eye-double-eff-eye-see
Triffic! TRIFFIC! TRIFFIC!
Yes it's me, ME, ME!

DUET FOR BLAUBOK AND QUAGGA

This goes with the Great Auk poem I wrote earlier. The Quagga was like half a horse and half a zebra and the Blaubok was a deer with a beautiful blueish colour to its coat. They lived in South Africa till the Europeans came. We shot them all. Hottentots was our name for the people who lived there already. We shot a good few of them too.

B: Nevermore
Q: Nevermore

B: When you see a world of space for us
Q: Can it be that there's no place for us?

B: Blaubok (echo) Blaubok
Q: Quagga (echo) Quagga

B: All our grace and our agility
Q: Yet you kill us with facility.

B: Blaubok (echo) Blaubok
Q: Quagga (echo) Quagga

B/Q: Colonise the spot that Time forgot
And rename it Holland Hottentot.
Show the Hottentot just what is what
With a rifle shot.

B: Blaubok (echo) Blaubok
Q: Quagga (echo) Quagga

B: Human skill and human cleverness
Q: Threw us into never-neverness.

B: Blaubok (echo) Blaubok
Q: Quagga (echo) Quagga

B/Q: Humankind comes out to civilise,
     Standardise and compartmentalise,
     Colonise and itemise merchandise.
     Something dies now.

B: Blaubok (echo) Blaubok
Q: Quagga (echo) Quagga

B/Q: Dead we are, there's no returning
     Till the sun and stars stop burning.

     Never.

HURRAH FOR THE UNIVERSE

This one is for Emma. There is a theory now that we are the only planet in the Universe that has any life on it at all but if that's so then what's all the rest of it FOR?

In days of old
the schools all told
that the earth was flat
and it looks like that
but it isn't so
for now we know
that it's globular

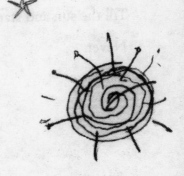

and the sun they said
in the days long dead
was a golden god
with a lightning rod
and a chariot
but we know it's not
for the sun's a star

and the stars are suns
and zillions
are being born
in capricorn
and a lot no doubt
are going out
like an old cigar

and astronomers say
light years away
spin other earths
with different births
and the people there
in the little bear
or andromeda

one day perhaps
by the great star maps
will come to see
what we may be
companions
from distant suns
who have come so far

and they might seem odd
like the golden god
or a purple sponge
or a blob of gunge
of enormous size
with a thousand eyes
peculiar

but we'll give a shout
if we're still about
that we're not alone
in the great unknown
and these strange others
are our sisters and our brothers
which is what they are.

HURRAH!
HURRAH!
HURRAH!

THE BLOAT FILES

Continued from page 109

The story so far: Horace Bloat,
ex-millionaire, has bought a National
Lottery ticket with his last pound.
There is a power cut as the draw is
being made. As he waits in the dark,
Horace has a funny feeling that he will
win the jackpot. Now read on:

Chapter Four

Funny feelings are all very well. But have you any IDEA
what the chances are of being the big winner in the
National Lottery if you buy just one ticket?

Let me tell you that they're a good deal less than your
chances of being struck by lightning in a thunderstorm.

This may be a fairy story but there are limits. The winning numbers were quite different from the ones
Horace Bloat had chosen.

They belonged to Mrs Penge who scooped the jackpot and won over forty million pounds.

Actually it was quite helpful to her as she had already
spent all Horace's fortune on a huge Wildlife Park for
Whales off the coast of Greenland.

It was two hundred and fifty miles long, one hundred
and twenty miles wide and seventeen miles deep.

Whales need lots of space and like to come and go as they please.

The forty million pounds came in very handy to build a submarine bathysphere powered by wind, waves and a hundred little green men on bicycles.

From her submarine bathysphere Mrs Penge observed whales in their natural habitat. She lived happily ever after down there and so did the whales.

'I've been poor and I've been rich,' said Mrs Penge to her favourite little green man whose name was Albert. 'And rich is better.'

Albert smiled and kept on pedalling. 'Phew!' was all he said.

But what happened to Horace? He lived in Ponder's End with his Auntie Pam who needed the company since her goldfish died.

Sometimes they quarrelled, but mostly they didn't. They bought a pair of budgies which are more fun than goldfish (or most people think so).

THE END

THE ACROSTIC VALENTINE

I just had to write this for you, Adam Burke. I can't disguise my feelings a minute longer. But I know that someone as busy and successful as you can hardly be expected to find out what acrostic means.

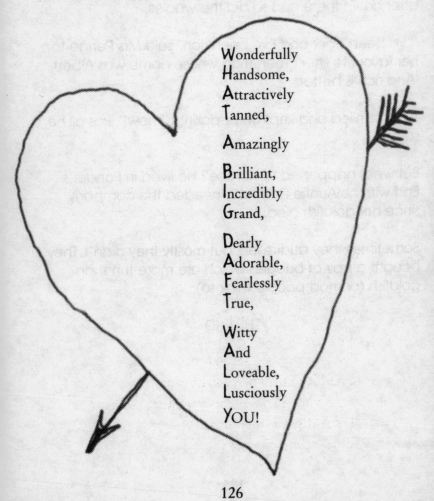

Wonderfully
Handsome,
Attractively
Tanned,

Amazingly

Brilliant,
Incredibly
Grand,

Dearly
Adorable,
Fearlessly
True,

Witty
And
Loveable,
Lusciously
YOU!

People often ask me, 'How do you write all those wonderful poems, Phoebe?' Or they would ask me if they weren't shy. Or stupid like some people. Anyway, this is how.

Unzip your head
And shake it all out.
What a bagful of rubbish!
But stir it about –
It's not rubbish at all.
It's a sackful of SWAG.
Let's look at the treasures
You've stuffed in your bag:

The smell of the roads
When they're putting down tar,
What Dad said when some wally
Crashed into his car,
The hedgehog that came
To the window last night,
How your best friend goes red
When you're having a fight,
The way the trees shake
When it's rainy and blusterous,
How your brother eats yoghurt
(It's really disgusterous),
What colour the sea is,

Not green and not blue,
And the thoughts that you think
For nobody but you.

What a bagful of rubbish?
No way! You can show 'em
And prove it's not rubbish by...

            WRITING A POEM.